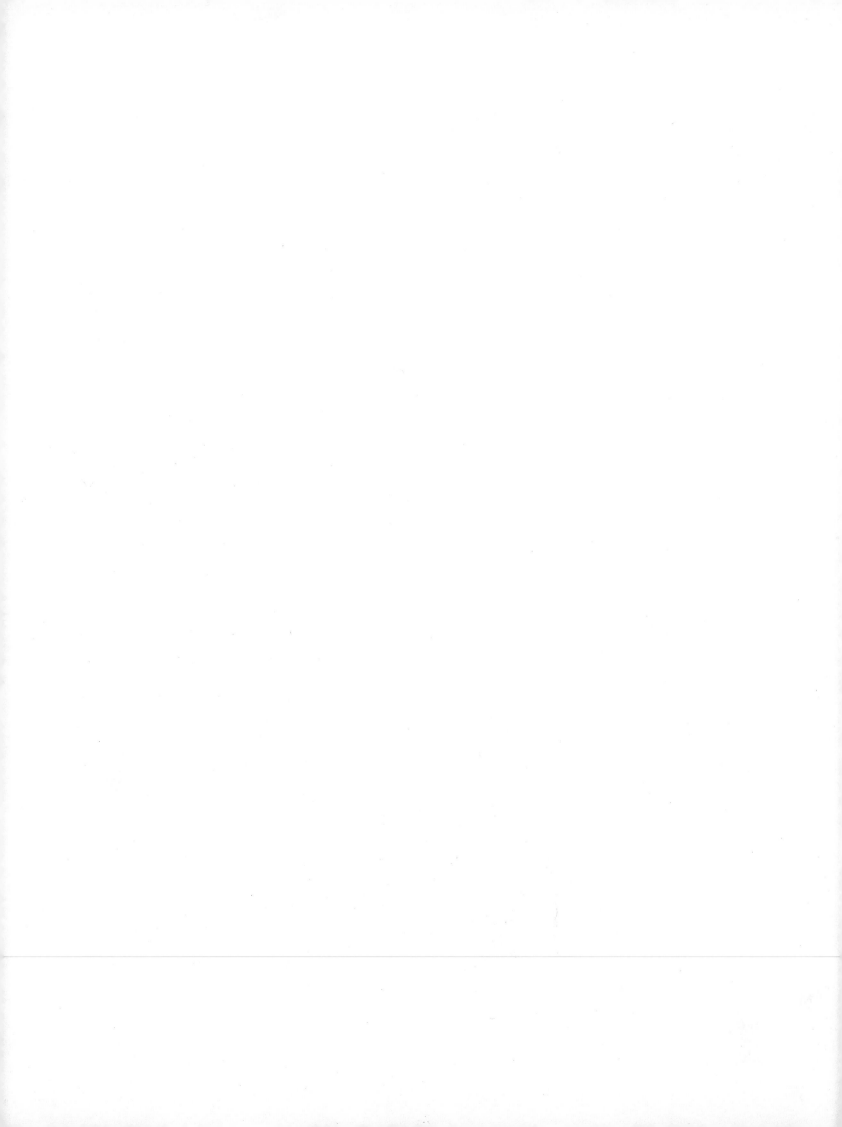

A B C
and
Counting

By Maureen Spurgeon

Illustrations by Pamela Storey

Turn the pages
And you'll see,
Just how easy
It can be
To learn your letters –
Numbers, too!
My friends and I
Will soon help you!
So, come along
And follow me!
We'll start off with
Your **a b c** !

A a

"Here I am, at my school –
We have lessons every day.
Is there something on my desk
Which begins with a letter **a**?
That's right! It's an **a**pple!
But, that isn't all –
Just look at the posters
Teacher's put on the wall!
There's an **a**nt, **a**lligator –
And an **a**rk, by the way . . .
An **a**crobat . . . what else
Begins with an **a**?"

Bb

"Lots of things here
Which begin with a **b**!
Barney **B**ear in his **b**oots –
And then – there is ME!
B is for **b**ear,
Birds and a **b**all,
A **b**us and a **b**icycle –
Now, is that all?
There are **b**elts on our coats
So, just look and see
How many more things
Begin with a **b**!"

Cc

"Picnic time, now!
And the next letter's **c**.
There are **c**ups for our drinks
And our **c**at – can you see?
We eat **c**arrots and **c**ake
And ripe **ch**erries, too!
And **ch**ocolate! Delicious!
Now, let me tell you –
Ch may be
Rather different a sound –
But the first letter's **c**.
Any more to be found?"

Dd

"Our next letter's **d**,
Which starts my **d**og's name –
He's **D**anny, the **d**og,
And he just loves a game!
Then there's **D**aisy the **d**onkey,
Another good friend.
She'll never bite
Or try to offend!
See **d**uck and the **d**ucklings,
And a big **d**ragonfly –
Any more letter **d** words?
Play a game of I-Spy!"

Ee Ff Gg Hh

"**E** is for **e**ggs,
For a breakfast-time dish.
F is for **f**lowers,
A **f**rog and some **f**ish!
And **f** is for **f**arm
Where my **G**randma, I see!
Her name, of course,
Begins with a **G** . . .
H is for **h**ens,
And a **h**orse eating **h**ay,
And a big **h**elicopter,
Flying swiftly away!"

Ii Jj Kk

"**I** is for **i**ce-cream –
My favorite treat!
Jack-in-the-Box
Would love some to eat!
His name, you know,
Begins with a **J** –
And a big **j**ug of **j**uice
Begins the same way!
Then there's **k** for **k**oala,
My **k**ite and a **k**ing,
And a **k**itten which makes
Knots in the **k**nitting!"

Ll

"**L** is for **l**aces –
One of mine is undone!
A strong **l**eash for Danny –
Every dog should have one.
There are **l**eaves on the trees
And **l**ettuce for tea,
A bright **l**adybug, and
A **l**ollipop for me!
Then a **l**adder for Daddy,
And some **l**etters, too,
Brought by the postman –
Any more words for you?"

Mm

"**M** is for **m**edicine
To take when we're ill –
The **m**oon through my window –
So bright and so still . . .
Then, **m** for the **m**ilk
Which **M**ommy brings me.
And I know there's a **m**ouse –
Take a look! Can you see?
Money and **m**oneybox,
Mushrooms – see them?
How many more things
Begin with an **m**?"

Nn Oo Pp

"Now we are out camping!
Can you see a **n**est!
A **n**ewspaper for Daddy –
That's what he likes best.
Nest and **n**ewspaper
Both begin with an **n** –
There are **n**uts and a **n**et,
What's the next letter, then?
It's **o** for an **o**wl!
And next comes a **p**,
Which begins **p**ath and **p**illows –
Any more? Look and see!"

Qq Rr Ss

"The next letter is **q**
Which begins the word **q**ueen –
Though, here in our park,
There's not one to be seen!
The **r**ain and the **r**abbits
Begin with – can you guess?
That's right! It's an **r**!
And the next letter's **s**
We have **s** for **s**ee-**s**aw,
A **s**lide and some **s**wings!
Look hard! You may notice
Quite a few other things!"

Tt Uu

"Now, the next letter
Is special to me.
Can you think just why?
It is letter **t**!
Yes! **T** for **T**eddy –
Television, too!
The **t**rack and a **t**unnel . . .
Now, the next letter's **u**
Which begins **u**mbrella
To help keep us dry,
When rain begins falling
From clouds in the sky."

Vv Ww

"**V** for the **v**iolin
Which my Daddy plays.
He's a fine **v**iolinist
Doing practice most days.
There's **v**olcano and **v**ase –
Both begin with a **v** –
W comes next –
Through the **w**indow, you'll see
The **w**ell, with the **w**ater
Which is for us all.
Then Daddy's **w**heelbarrow,
Which he's left by the **w**all!"

Xx Yy Zz

"Now, **x** for the **x**ylophone
I'd like to play!
I had one, you see,
For my birthday, today!
Letter **x** often ends words –
Like si**x**, fi**x** and fo**x** . . .
Then, **y** for my **y**acht –
It was packed in a bo**x**!
Tomorrow, I'm taking it
Out for a sail!
Then **z** is for **z**ebra,
With stripes to his tail!"

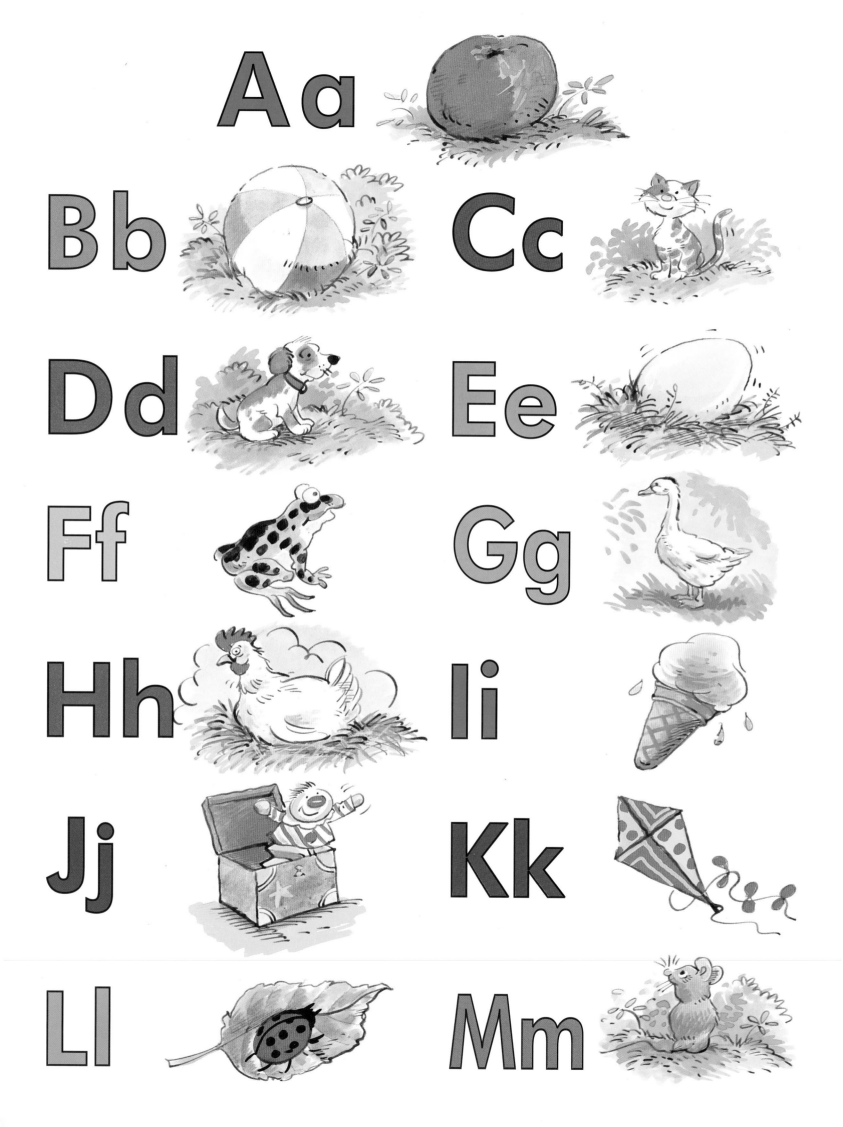

So, it's as easy
As can be
To learn your **a b c**
With me!
But, that's not all
That we can do –
And, as we play,
We shall learn, too!
So, come along,
And join in the fun!
You'll be surprised
At what can be done!

The next thing to do
Is to count **1 2 3**,
Will you come to my party
And count things with me?
Counting to ten
Is easy to do!
Mommy Bear showed me,
So I know that it's true.
And when it's all ready
You'll very soon see
How easy it is
To count, **1 2 3** !

1 one

"It's my birthday, today!"
Teddy cries out with glee.
"And lots of my friends
Are coming to tea!"
"But," says his Mommy,
"I need your help, too!
There's lots of counting
I want you to do!"
"One birthday cake!"
Mommy Bear thinks.
One is such a nice number,
But what can we drink?

2 two

"Here's your drink, Teddy!"
Mommy says with a smile,
"There's enough here to last
Your friends quite a while!
Two big jugs of cool lemonade!
Lots more in the kitchen!
It's all freshly made!"
"One cake, two jugs!
One, two!" Teddy cries.
"What's next to be counted?
Another surprise?"

2 =

3 three

When they go back inside,
Mommy Bear piles up high
Three dishes with chips!
Teddy gives a glad cry.
"One, two, three dishes!"
Mommy says, "Yes, that's right!
Take them into the garden!
No taking a bite!"
"So, one birthday cake,
And two jugs! One, two!
And three dishes!" says Teddy.
"Now, what shall I do?"

3 =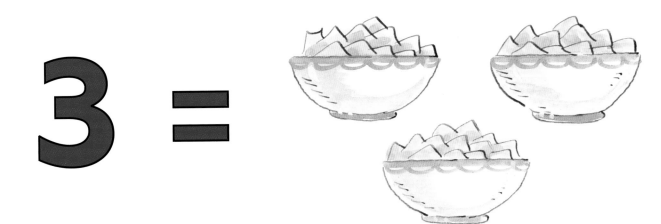

4 four

"Birthday candles!" smiles Mommy.
"We need three and one more . . ."
Teddy shouts out, "I know!
That's one, two, three, four!
Four candles, Mommy!
And I'm four, today!"
And he hands them to her,
To go on display!
They look nice on the cake –
He's as pleased as can be!
What's the next number?
Teddy can't wait to see!

4 =

5 five

One, two, three, four –
Five plates of cheese!
Mommy says, "Try a piece!"
Teddy answers, "Yes, please!"
At once, he decides
It's delicious to eat –
A tasty surprise,
And a savory treat!
Outside, comes a cry –
"We've arrived, Teddy Bear!"
And Mommy Bear smiles,
"Your next number's there!"

5 =

6 six

As Mommy Bear speaks,
The garden gate clicks . . .
"My friends!" shouts out Teddy.
"There ought to be six!
One, two, three, four,
Five, six!" Teddy grins.
"Here, have a balloon!
Now, my party begins!"
"Well, count the balloons!"
Mommy says. "One, two, three."
"Four, five, six!" joins in Teddy,
As pleased as can be!

6 =

7 seven

"Inside, for a moment!"
Calls Mommy Bear.
"Each of you will need
To take out a chair!
Teddy, six for your friends,
Then one for you!
So, there should be seven!"
He sees if that's true . . .
"One, two, three, four,
Five, six, seven chairs!
We've got one chair each!
What's next for us bears?"

7 =

8 eight

"Party hats!" smiles Mommy,
And in through the gate,
Comes Teddy's own Daddy,
He hopes he's not late.
"Now for the party hats,
Let's try them for size.
Yours doesn't count, Mommy!"
Teddy Bear cries,
"One, two, three, four, five,
Six, seven, eight!
Now let's have some lemonade,
Before it's too late!"

8 =

9 nine

"Teddy," smiles Mommy,
"We shall each need a straw –
That's eight straws for us,
Then, for Daddy, one more!"
Teddy Bear counts them out –
He's doing just fine!
"One, two, three, four, five,
Six, seven, eight, nine!
Nine straws, Mommy Bear,
To go in our drinks!"
"Now, what's the next number?"
Teddy Bear thinks . . .

9 =

10 ten

"Each friend's brought a present,
So I know that is six . . ."
Teddy would hate
To get into a fix . . .
"Then – two presents from Mommy,
From Daddy, two more . . .
So, if I am right,
That should make it four . . .
So, that's six, add on four . . ."
Teddy counts up again.
"One, two, three, four, five, six,
Seven, eight, nine, ten!"

10 =

There's a kite! And a ball!
A car and a train!
A boat and a drum
And a little toy plane,
A puppet, some pencils –
A bicycle, too!
Then everyone sings,
"Happy Birthday to you!"
"Oh, thank you!" cries Teddy.
And he counts up again.
"One, two, three, four, five,
Six, seven, eight, nine, ten!"

"So, that's one birthday cake,
Two jugs, lemonade,
Three dishes of chips,
Four candles displayed!
Five plates of cheese,
With six friends to share!
That's seven little teddies –
Each one needs a chair!
Eight party hats –
And nine straws for drinks,
Then come ten presents –
That's great!" Teddy thinks.

Now, his friends have all gone,
Teddy gets into bed,
Looking round at his cards –
A real sleepyhead!
"Today, I was four,
I'll be five next year!"
He tells himself, softly,
So that no one can hear.
Then he closes his eyes,
And counts, once again –
But he's fast asleep
Long before number ten!

1

2

3

4

5

6

7

8

9

10

There'll be lots of birthdays
For me – and for you!
But this one was special –
And lots of fun, too!
Now, we can tell
How to count up to **TEN**.
And if you forget,
You'll remember again
If you read the story
And count up the ways
My birthday became
The happiest of days!

So, we started off
Learning our **a b c**
And now we can count
Right from **1 2 3** !
Numbers and letters –
Both are the same,
Each can be learned
Like playing a game.
So, now you know,
Learning your **1 2 3**
Is just as easy
As your **a b c** !